COLOR ∗ CUT OUT ∗ SEND

ANIMAL
GREETING CARDS
COLORING BOOK

M.D. WHALEN

artwork by
FLORENTINO GOPEZ

MW00945885

THIS BOOK BELONGS TO

©2020 Top Floor Books

All rights reserved. No part of this publication may be
reproduced, transmitted, or stored in an information retrieval
system in any form or by any means, graphic, mechanical, or
electronic, including photocopying, taping, recording, without
permission in writing from the publisher.

ISBN 978 962 7866 48 0
First edition, published 2020

Top Floor Books
PO Box 29
Silvermine Bay, Hong Kong
topfloorbooks.com

INSTRUCTIONS

COLOR

CUT OUT

FOLD

CARD

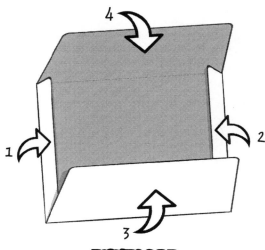

1 2 3 4

ENVELOPE

SEND!

MATERIALS

CRAYONS

COLORED PENCILS

GEL PENS

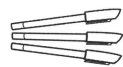

NOT RECOMMENDED

Markers, paint, or liquid ink can leak through the paper

Put a thick piece of paper under the page so the colors don't bleed through.

HINT: Lay a ruler against the dotted lines, then lightly scratch a pin along the edge. Now it folds straight!

© Top Floor Books

THIS CARD COLORED BY

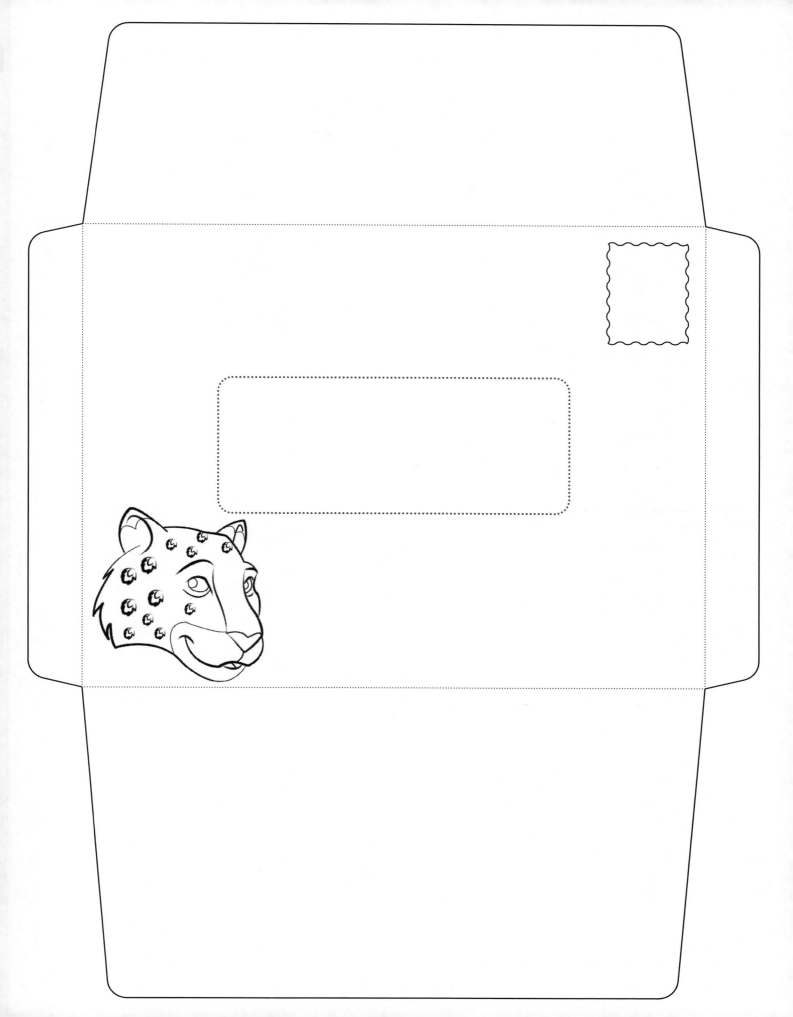

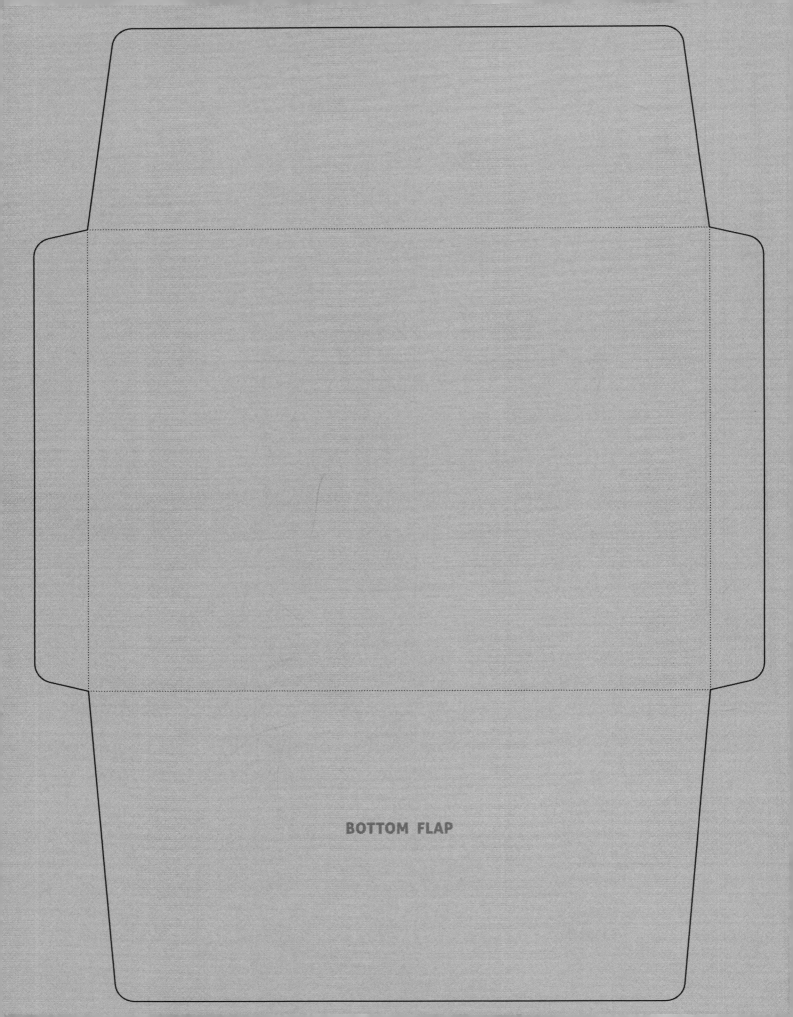

BOTTOM FLAP

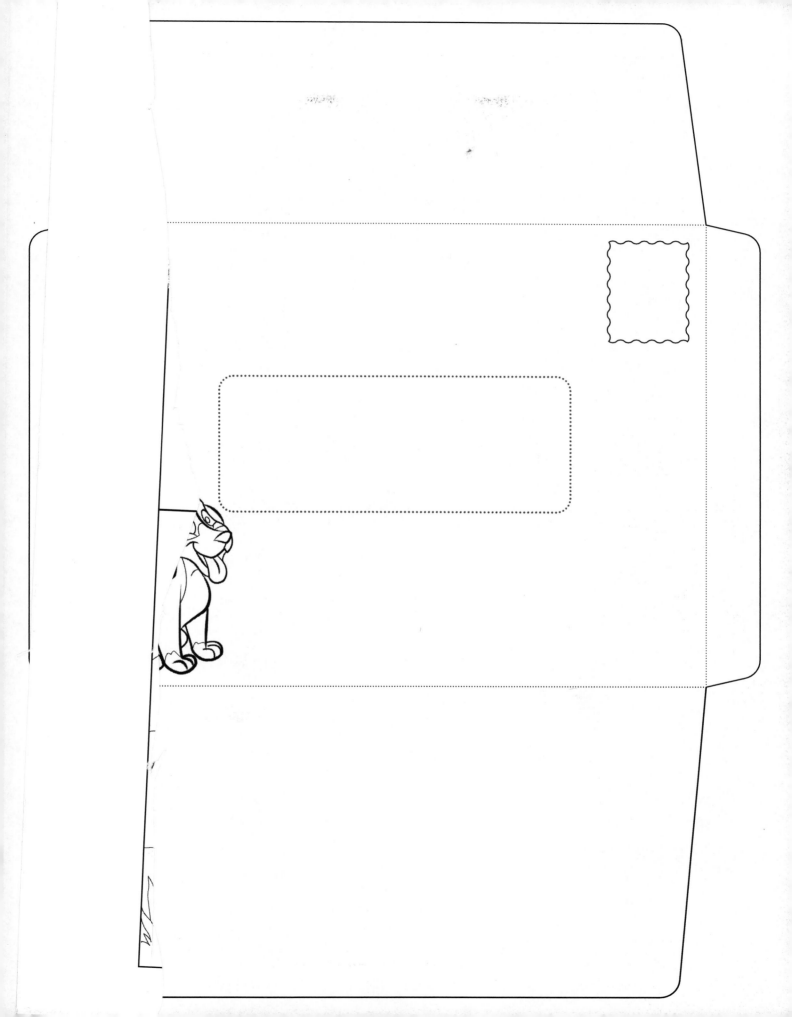

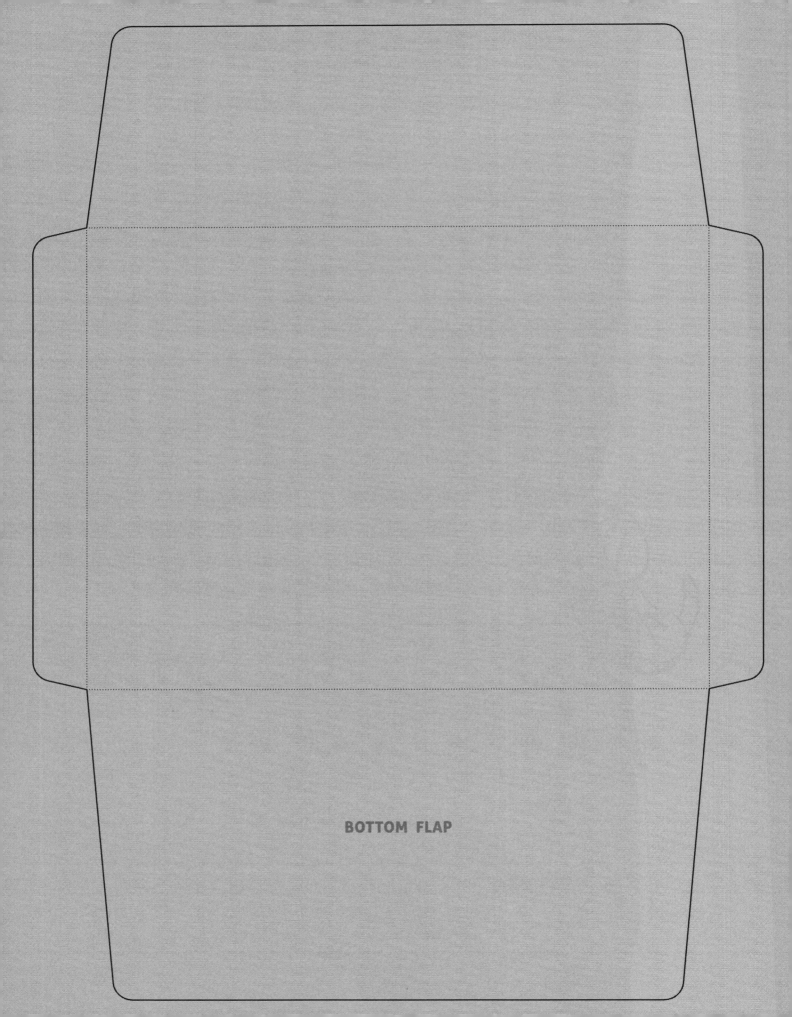

BOTTOM FLAP

© Top Floor Books

THIS CARD COLORED BY

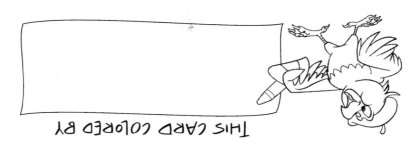

DON'T BEE A STRANGER!

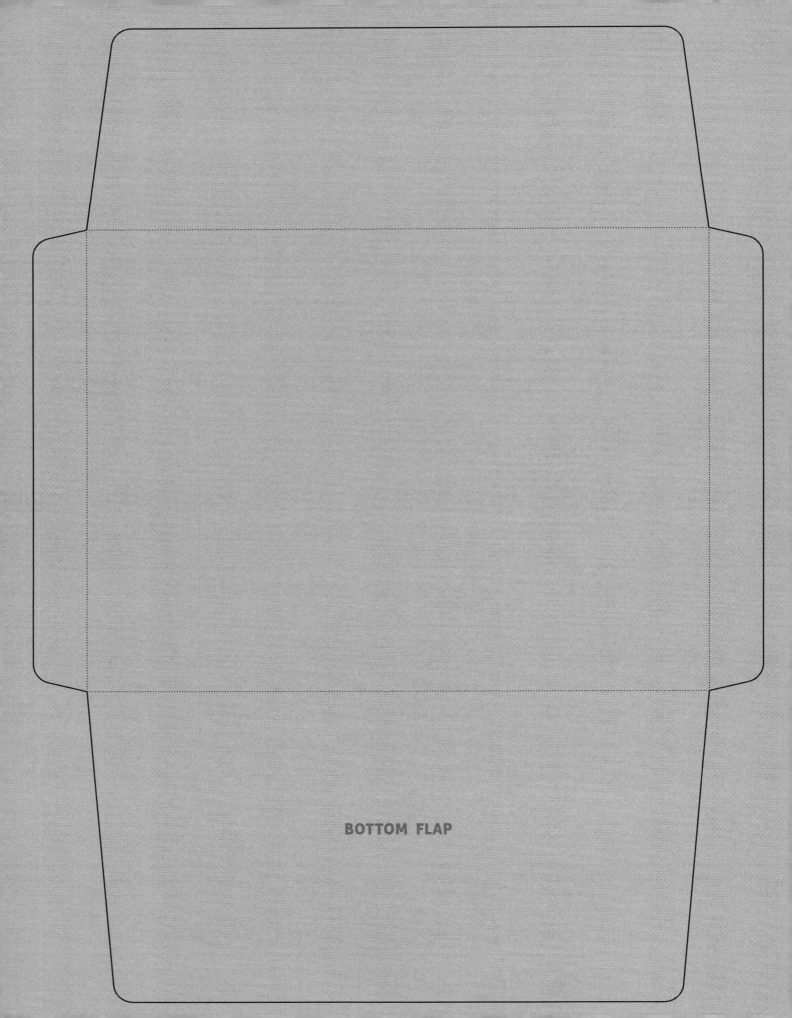

BOTTOM FLAP

THIS CARD COLORED BY

© Top Floor Books

SMILE!

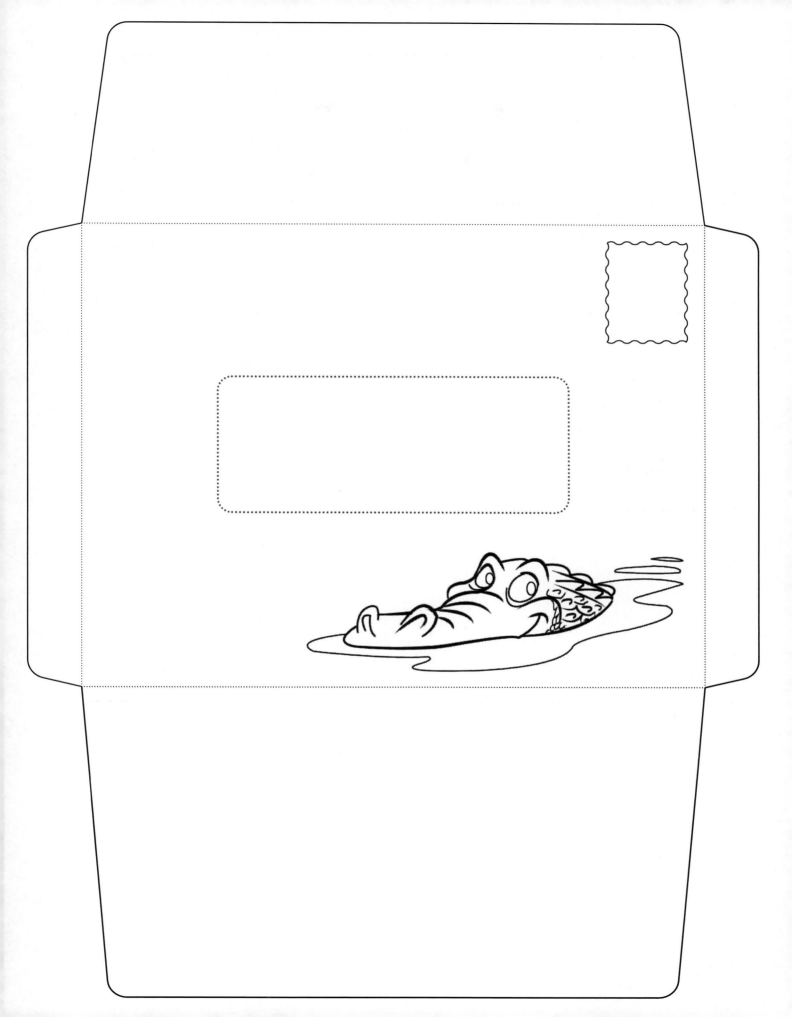

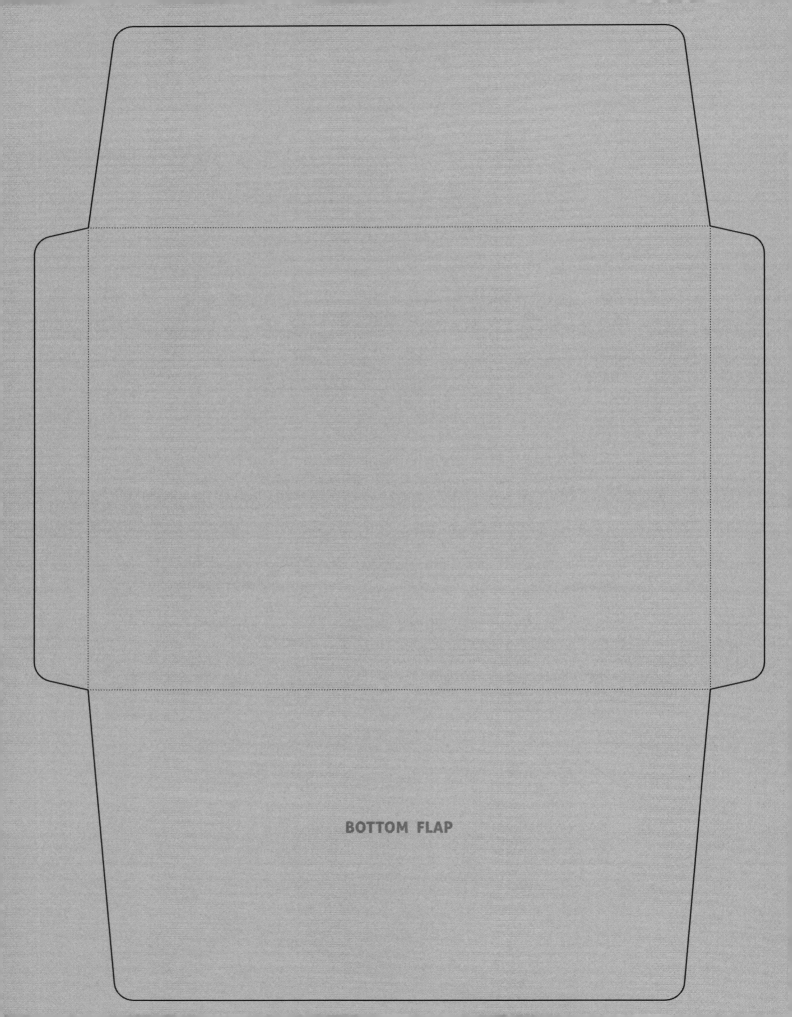

BOTTOM FLAP

© Top Floor Books

THIS CARD COLORED BY

YOU'RE ALMOST PURR-FECT

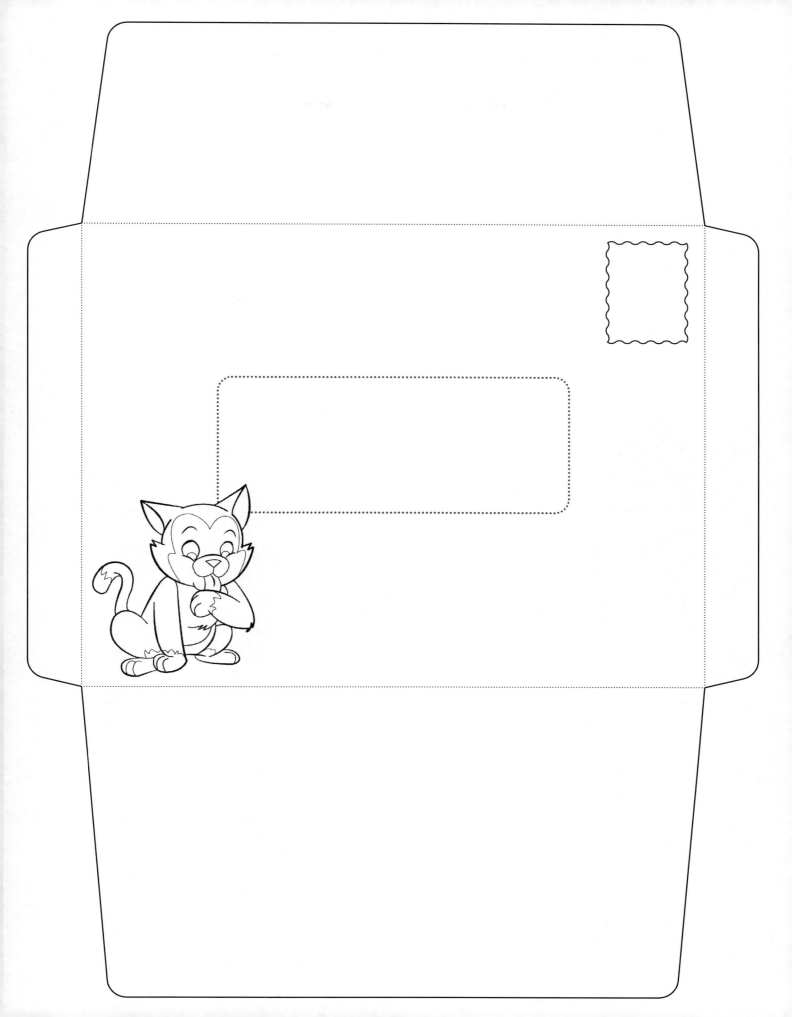

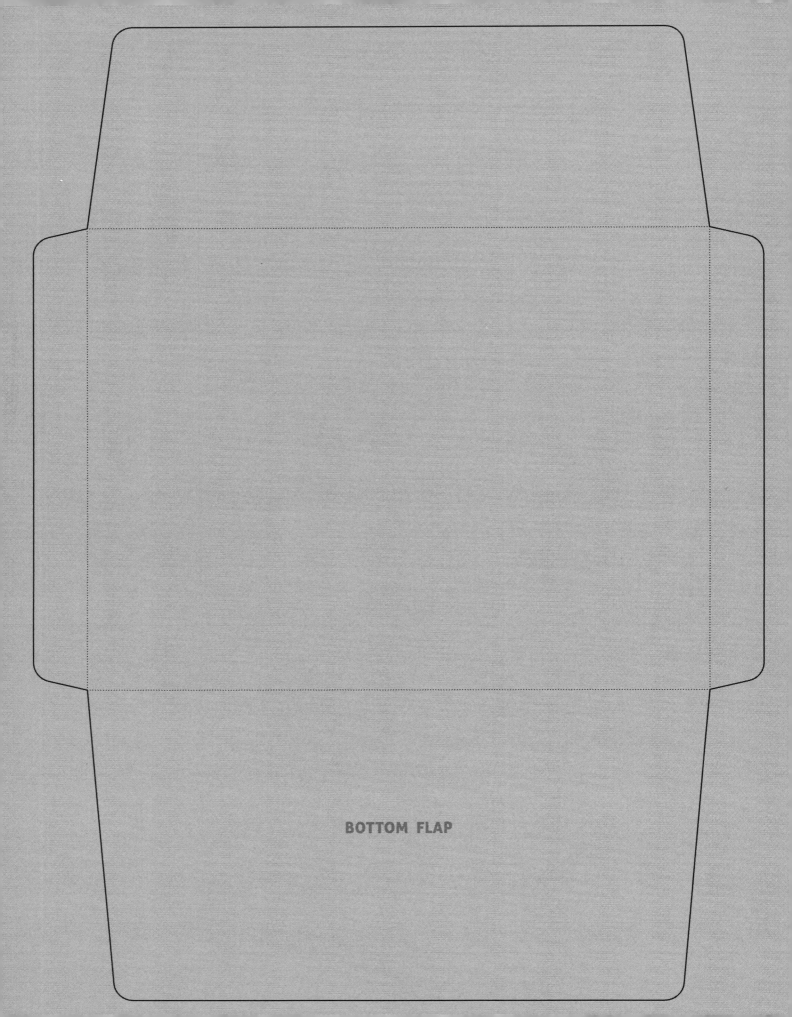

BOTTOM FLAP

© Top Floor Books

THIS CARD COLORED BY

BOTTOM FLAP

THIS CARD COLORED BY

© Top Floor Boooks

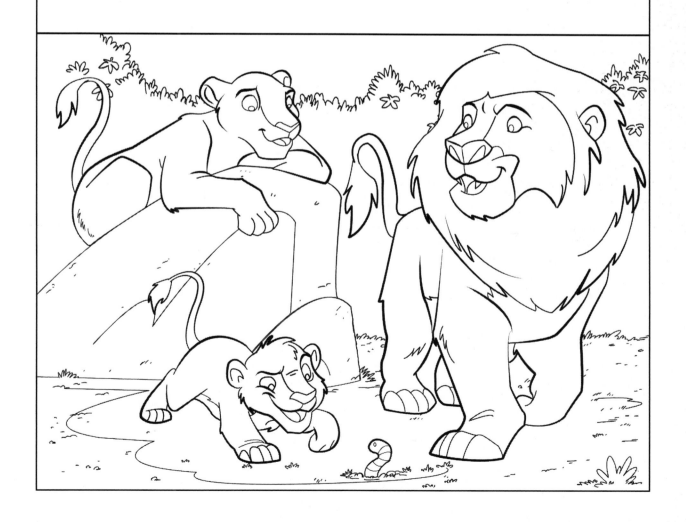

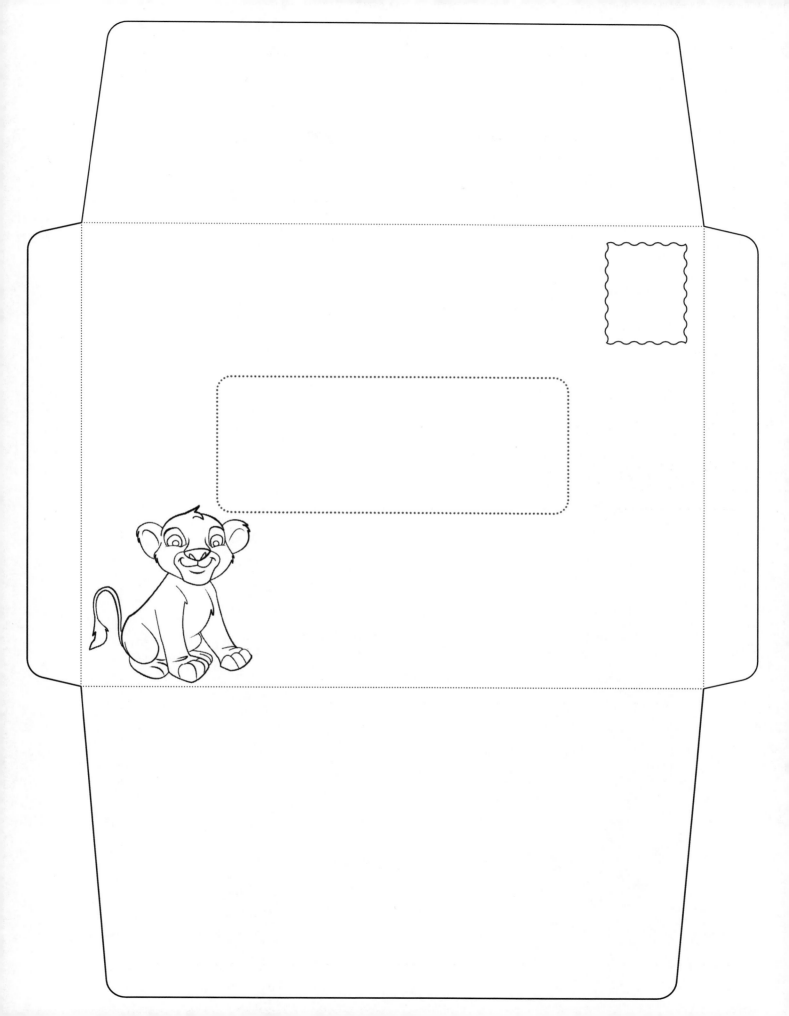

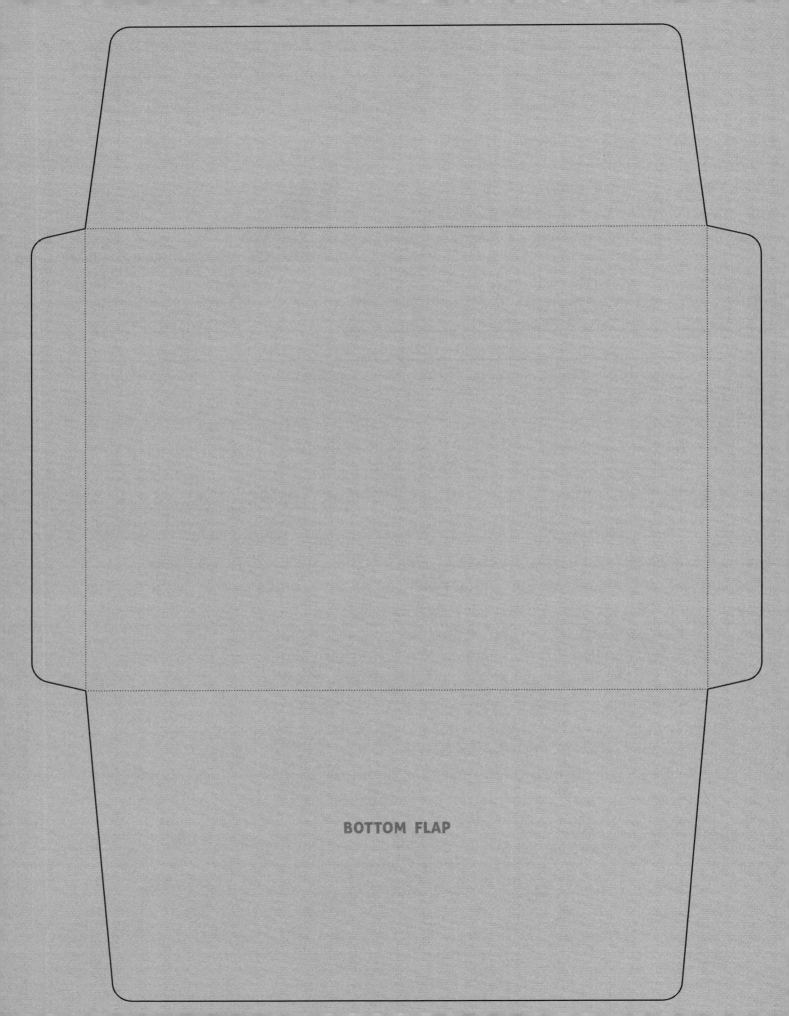

BOTTOM FLAP

THIS CARD COLORED BY

© Top Floor Books

OUR FRIENDSHIP IS NO TALL TALE

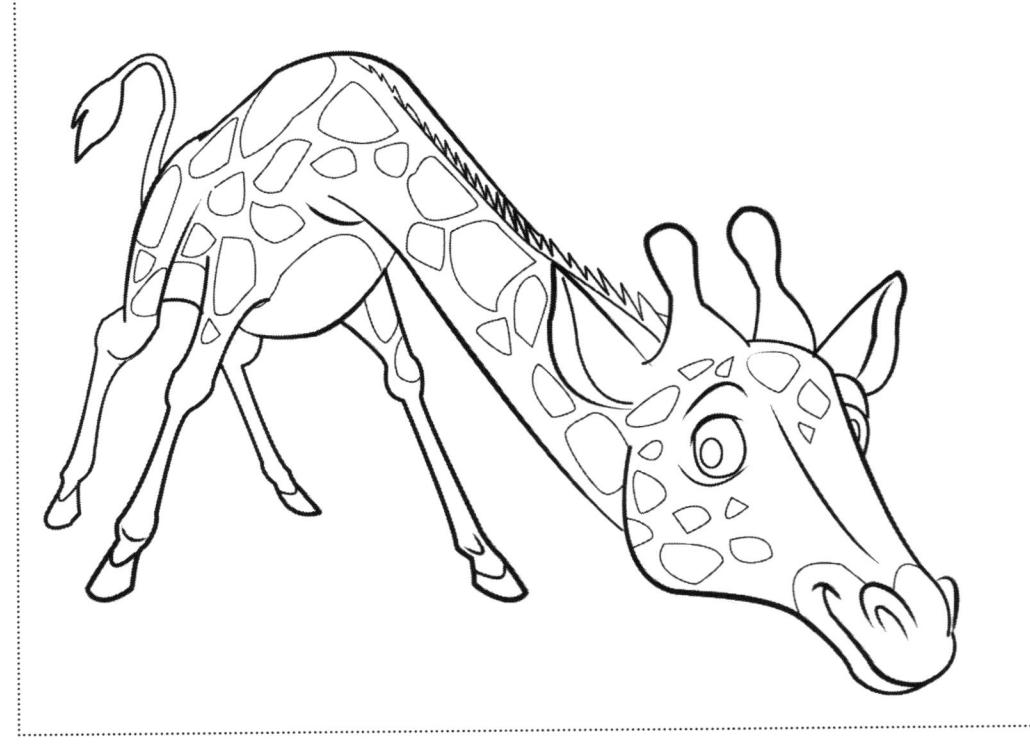

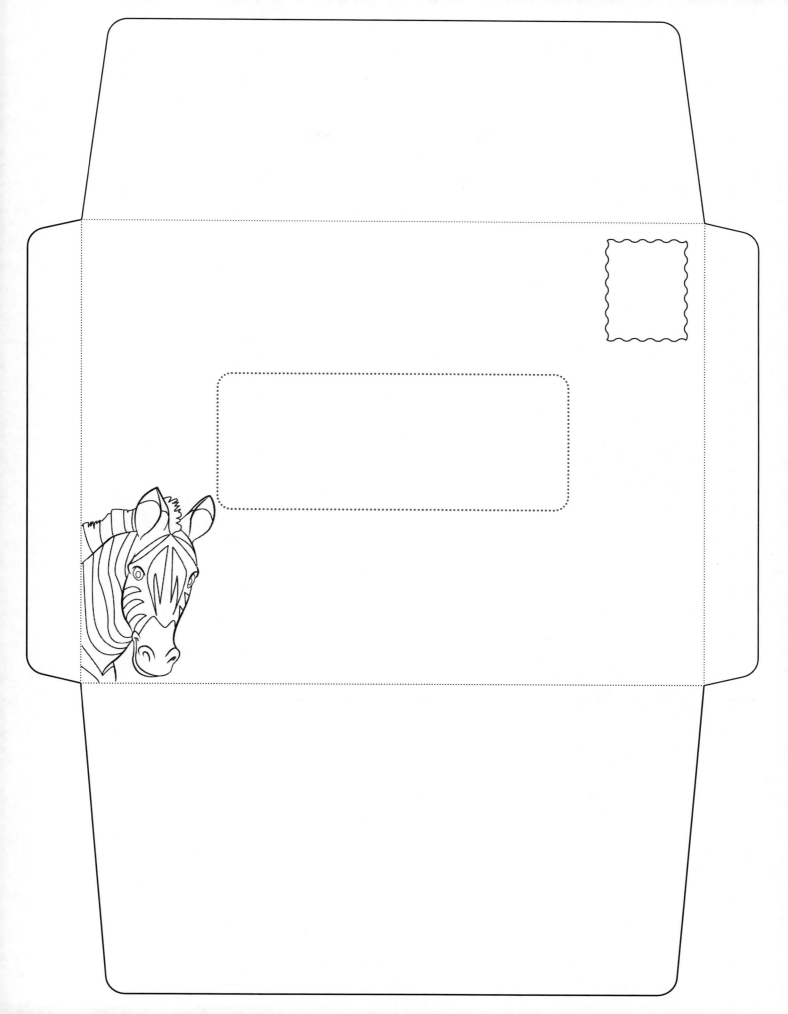

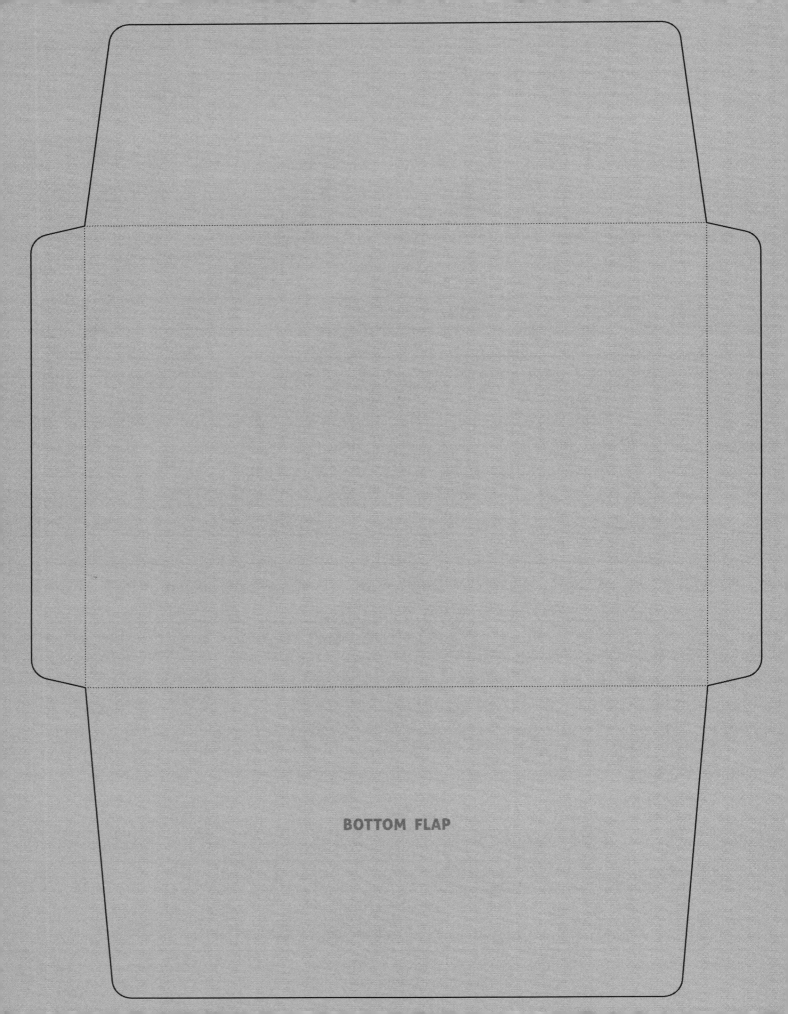

BOTTOM FLAP

© Top Floor Books

THIS CARD COLORED BY

YOU QUACK ME UP

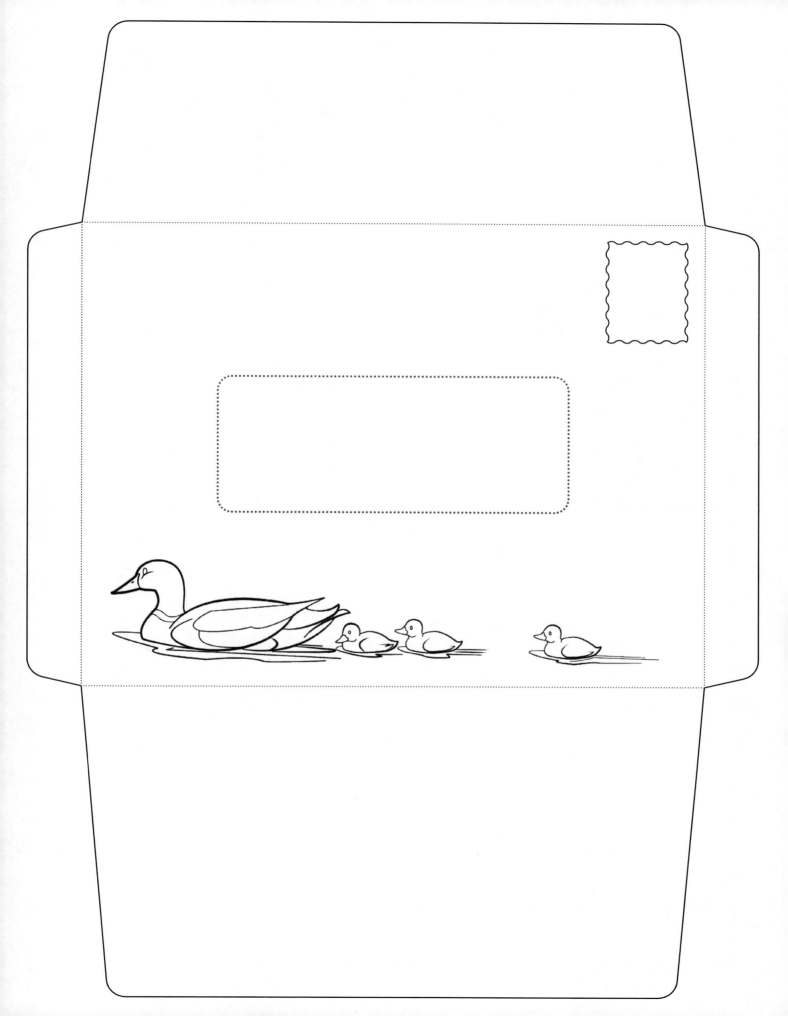

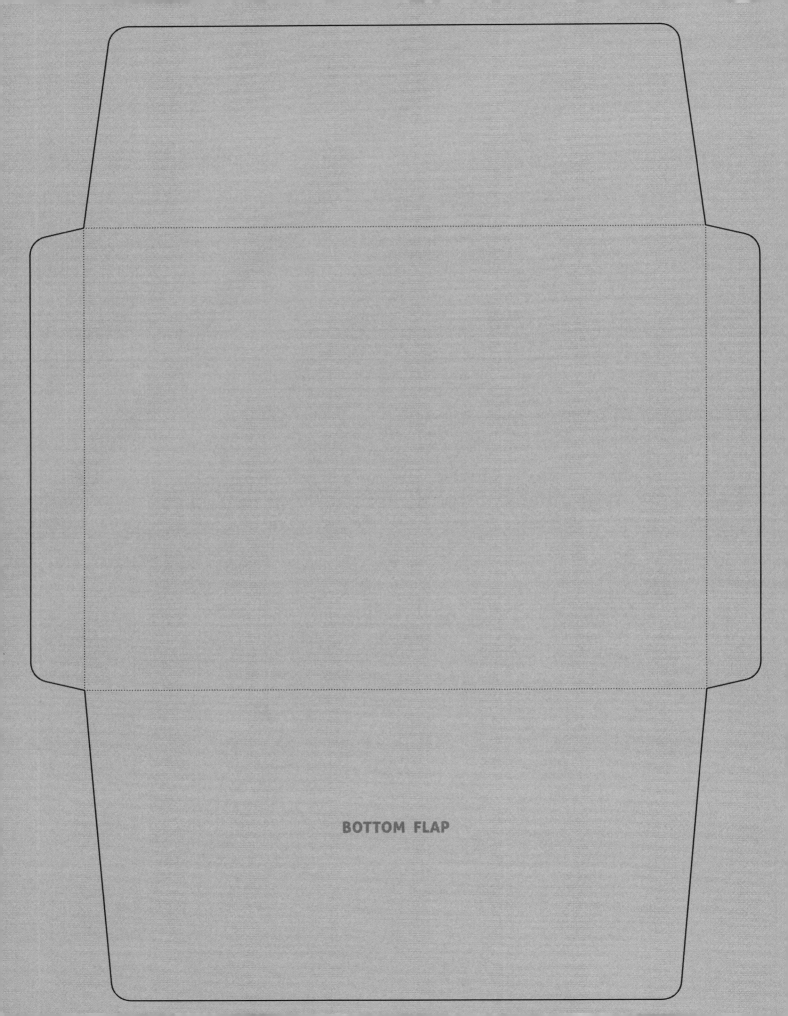

BOTTOM FLAP

THIS CARD COLORED BY

© Top Floor Books

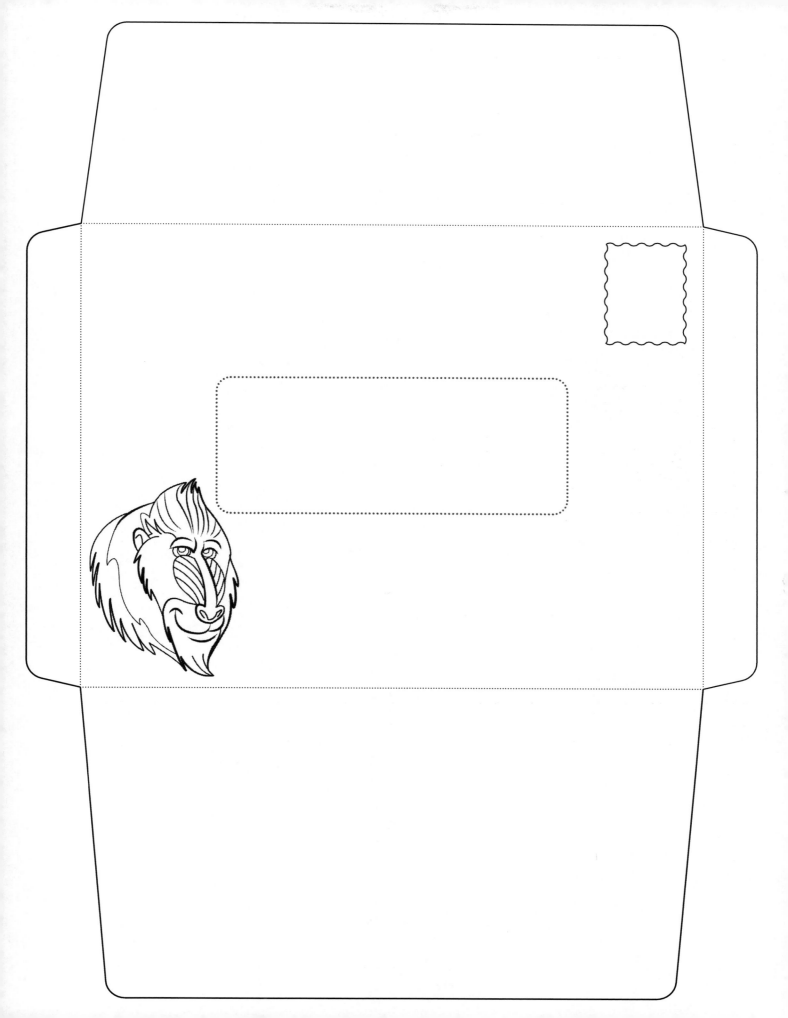

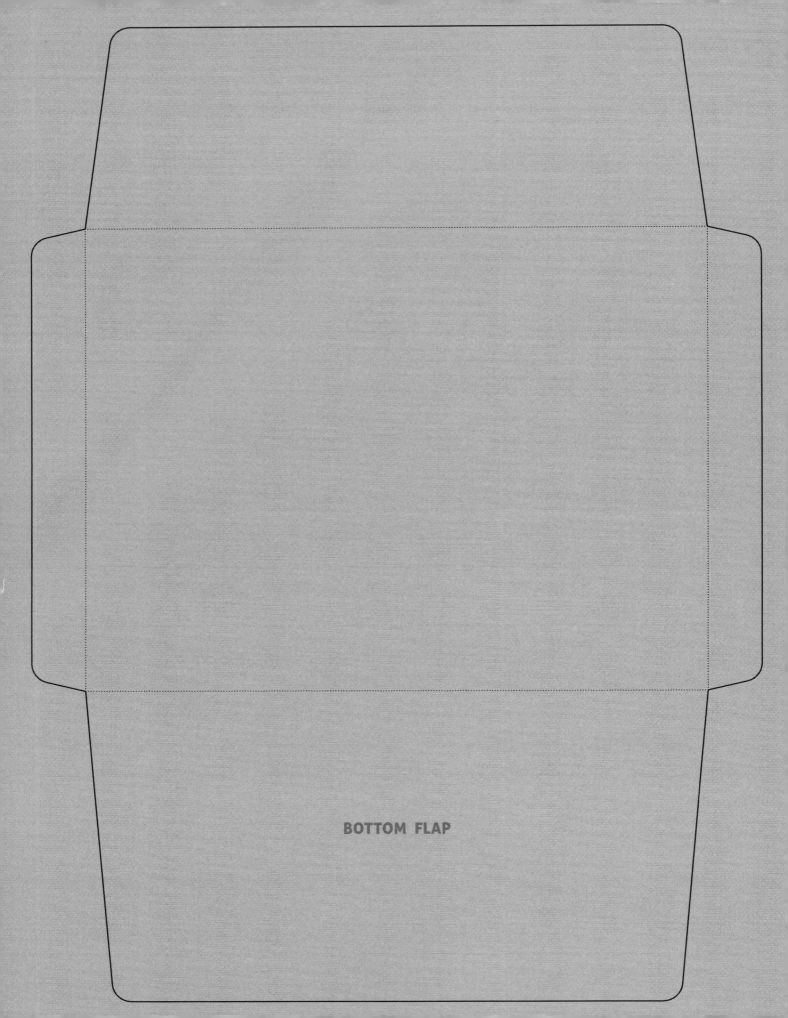

BOTTOM FLAP

THIS CARD COLORED BY

© Top Floor Books

WANT TO HORSE
AROUND?

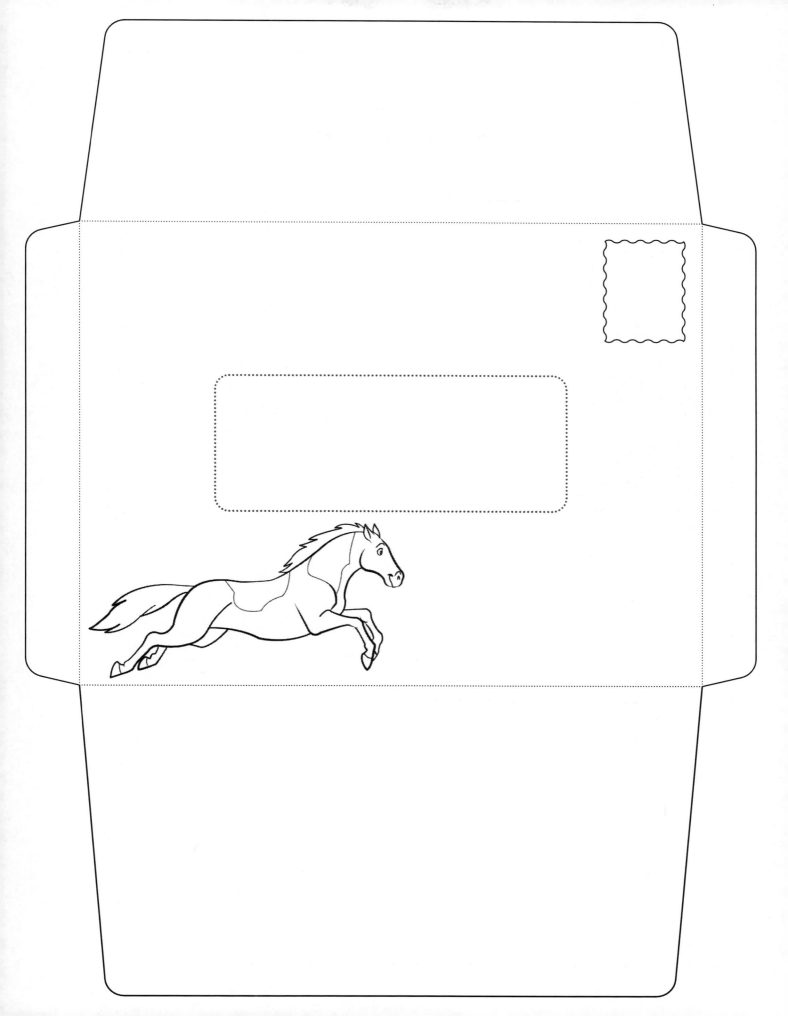

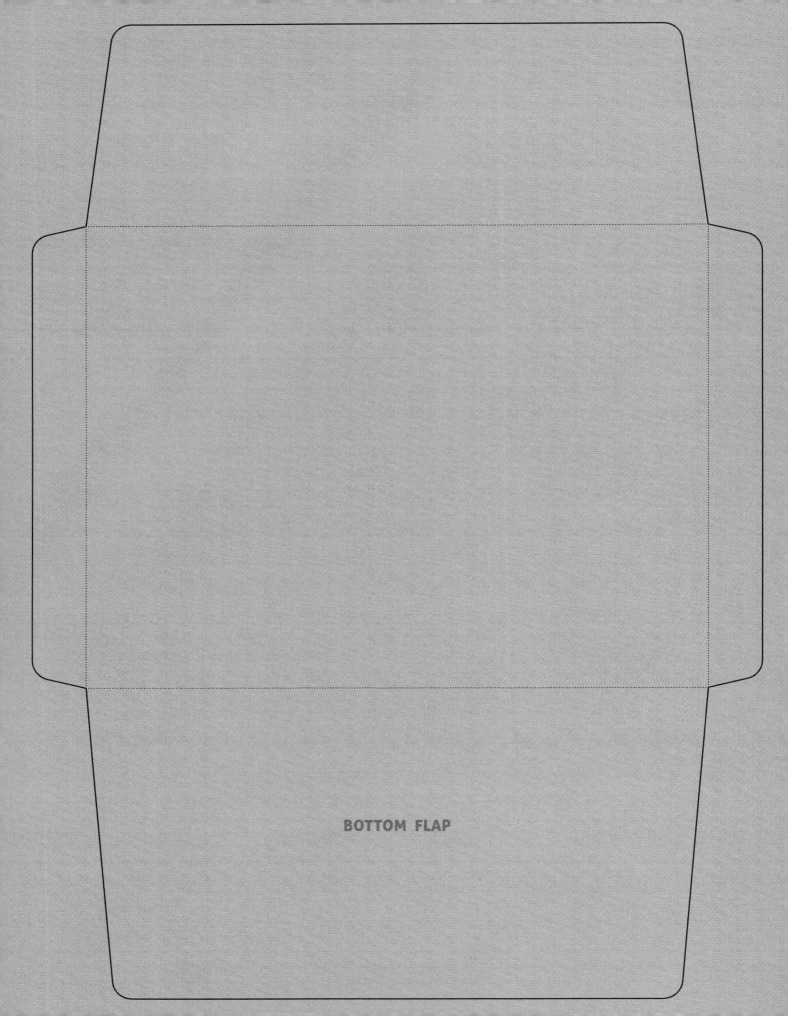

BOTTOM FLAP

© Top Floor Books

THIS CARD COLORED BY

Drop in any time!

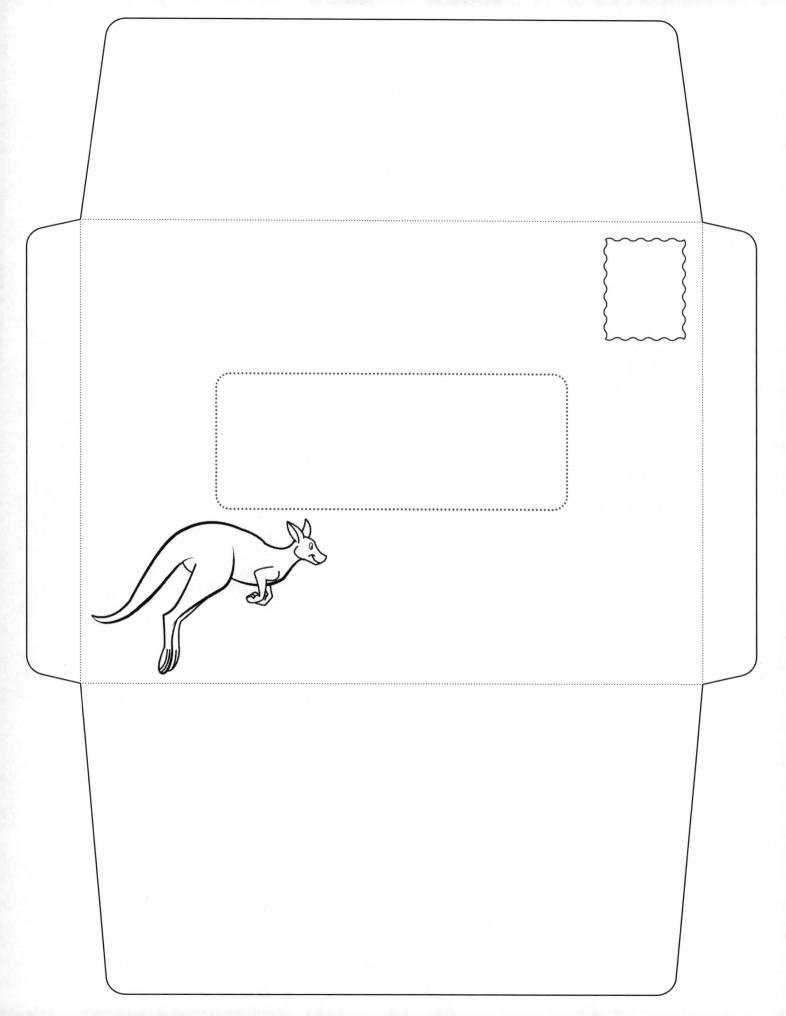

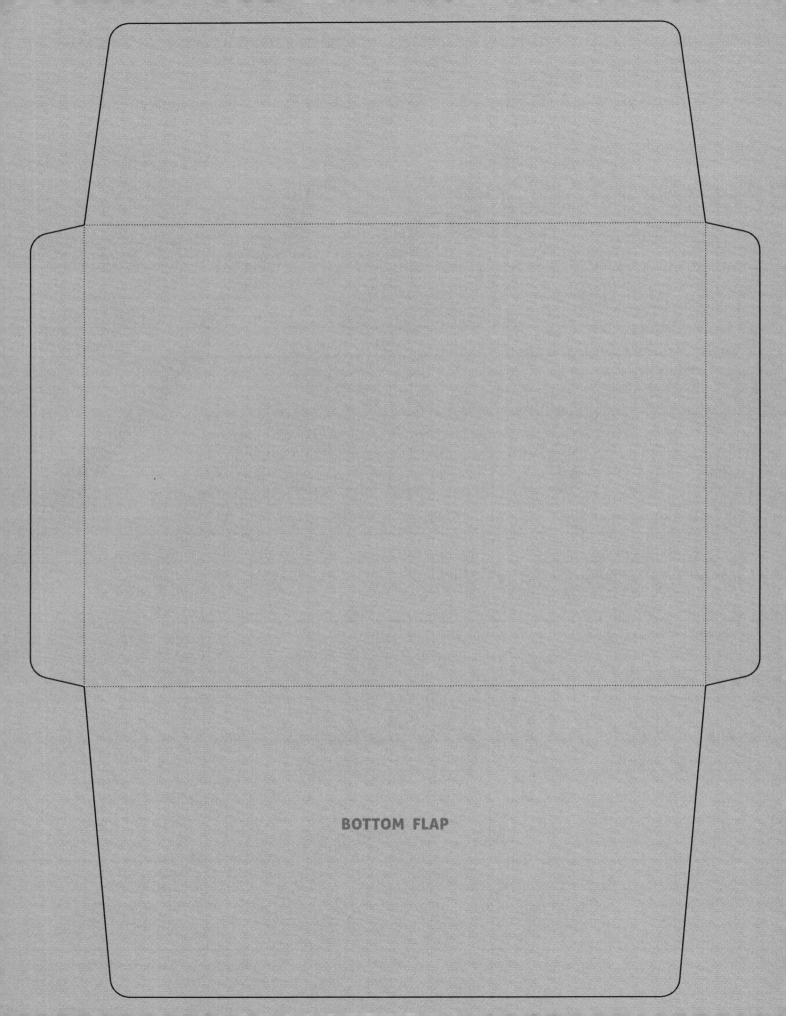

BOTTOM FLAP

THIS CARD COLORED BY

© Top Floor Books

YOU'RE A REAL
HOOT

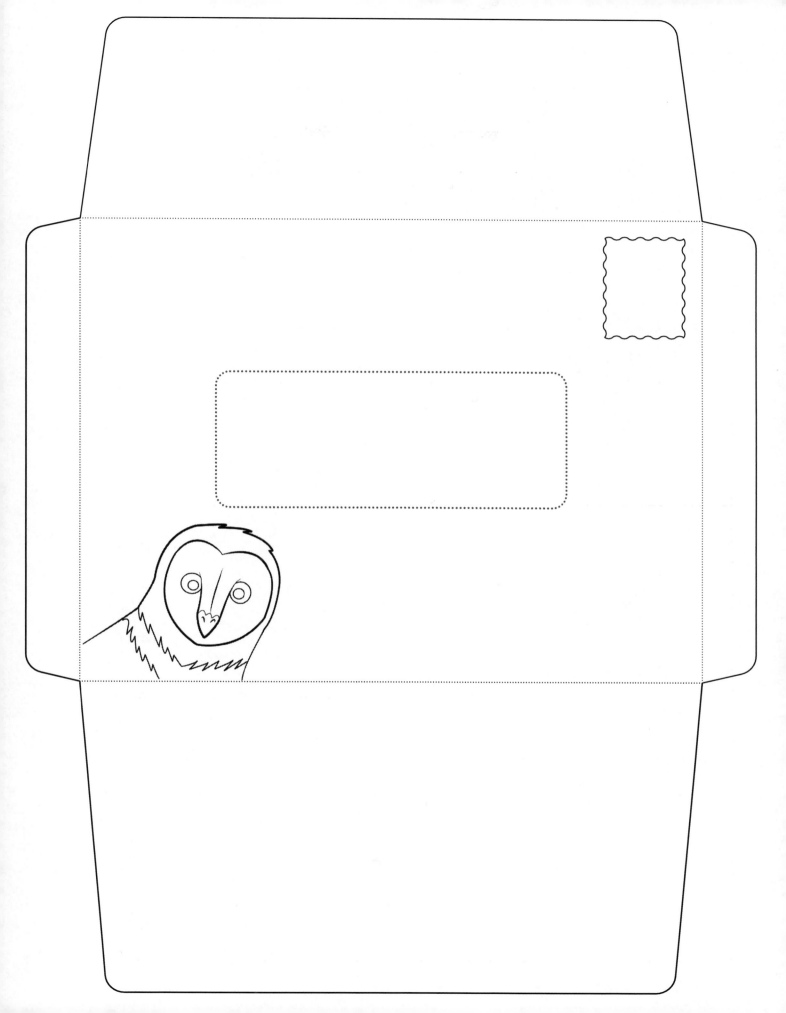

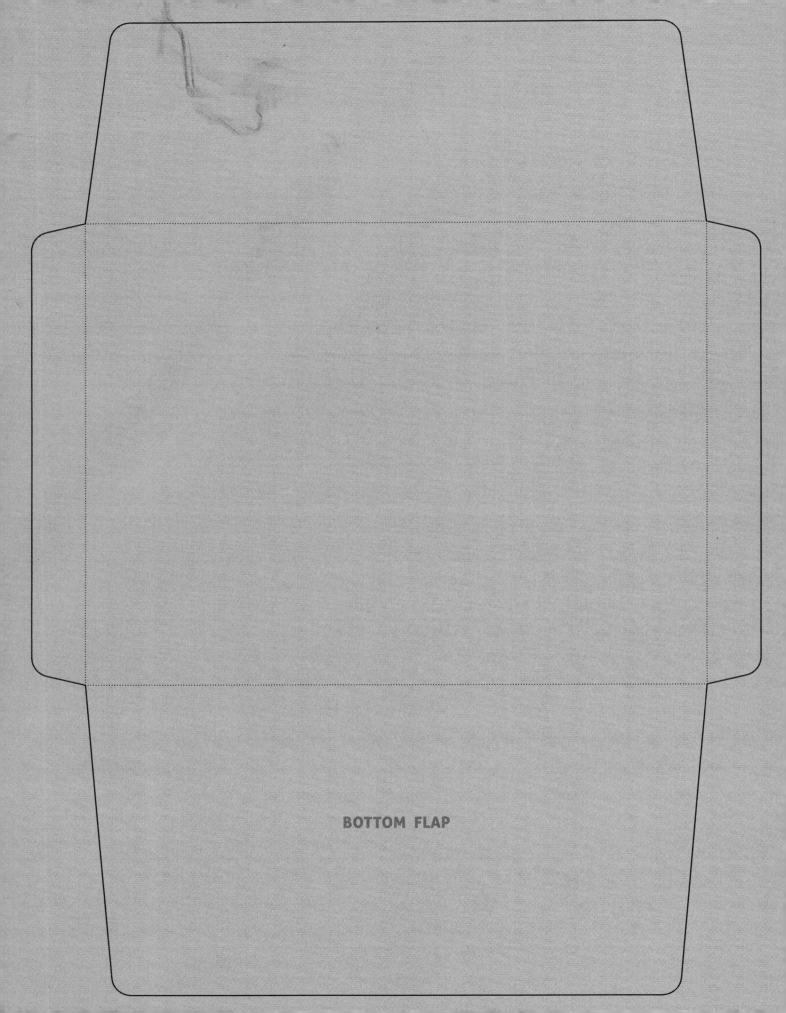

BOTTOM FLAP

© Top Floor Books

THIS CARD COLORED BY

I'M YOUR BIGGEST FAN

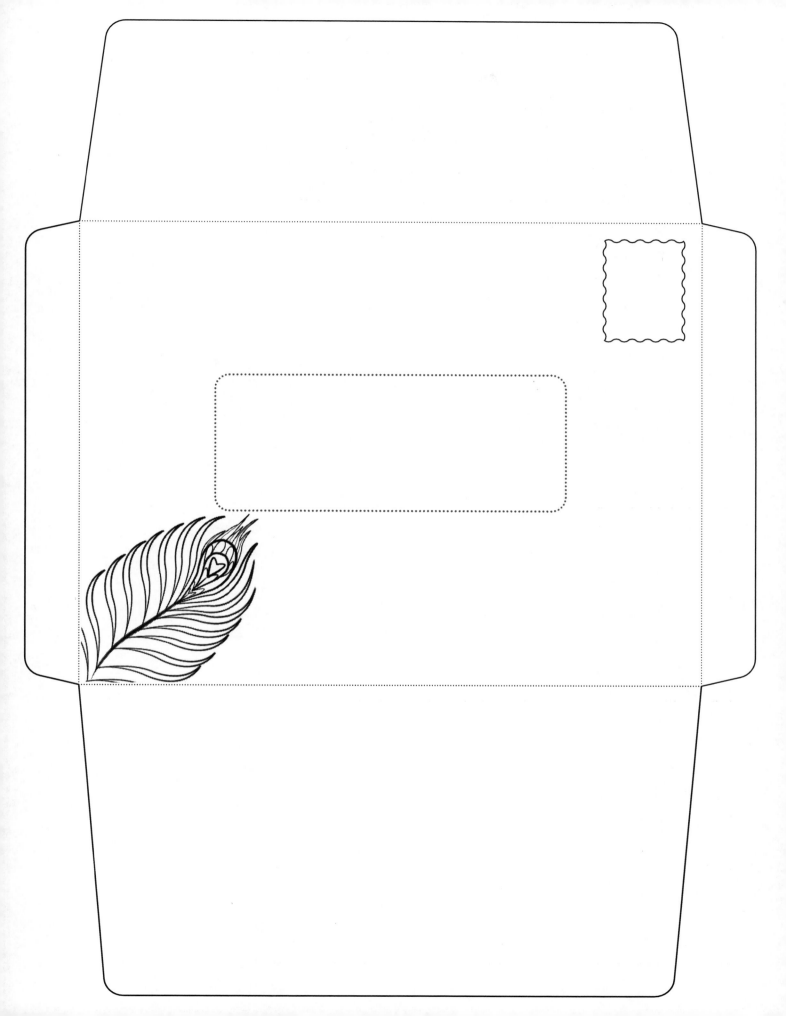

BOTTOM FLAP

© Top Floor Books

THIS CARD COLORED BY

FRIENDS FOREVER

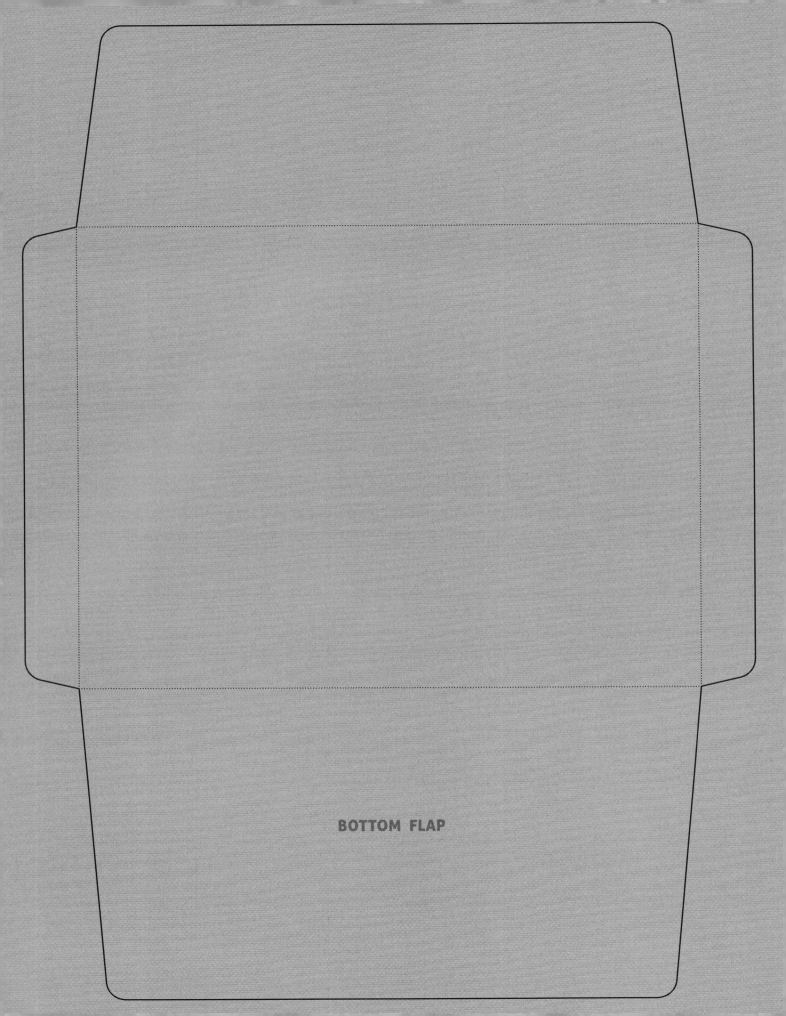

BOTTOM FLAP

© Top Floor Books

THIS CARD COLORED BY

You drive me NUTS

BOTTOM FLAP

THIS CARD COLORED BY

© Top Floor Books

I LIKE YOU TONS

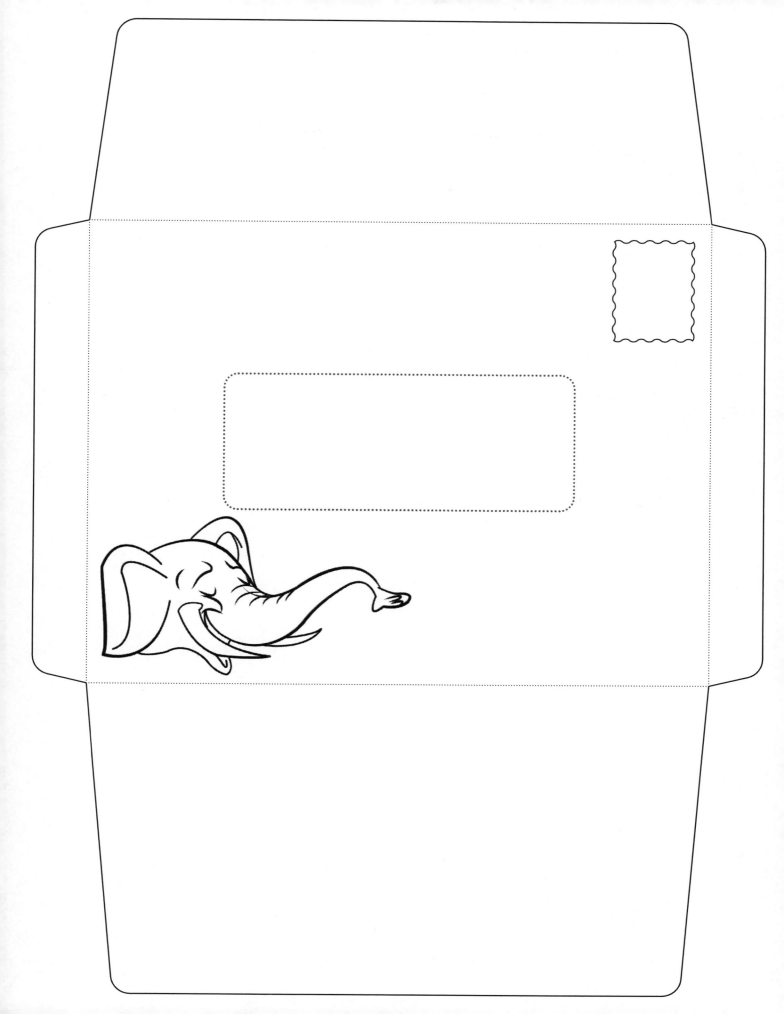

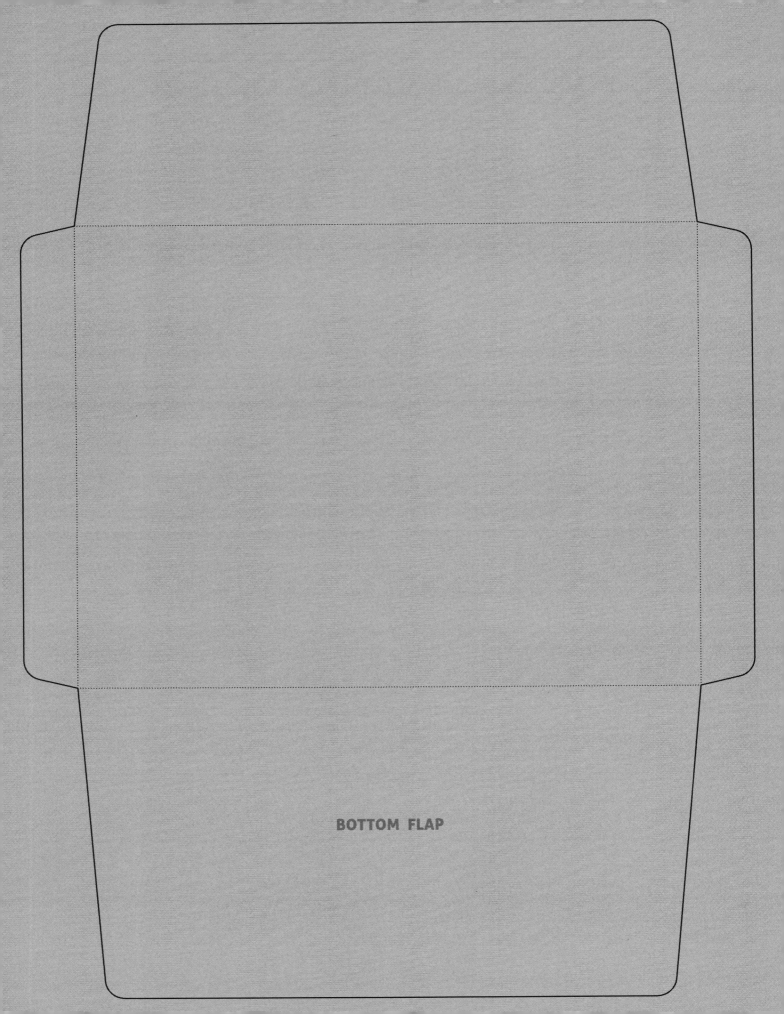

BOTTOM FLAP

THIS CARD COLORED BY

© Top Floor Books

Long time no sea!

BOTTOM FLAP

© Top Floor Books

THIS CARD COLORED BY

You're HISSSSS-sterical!

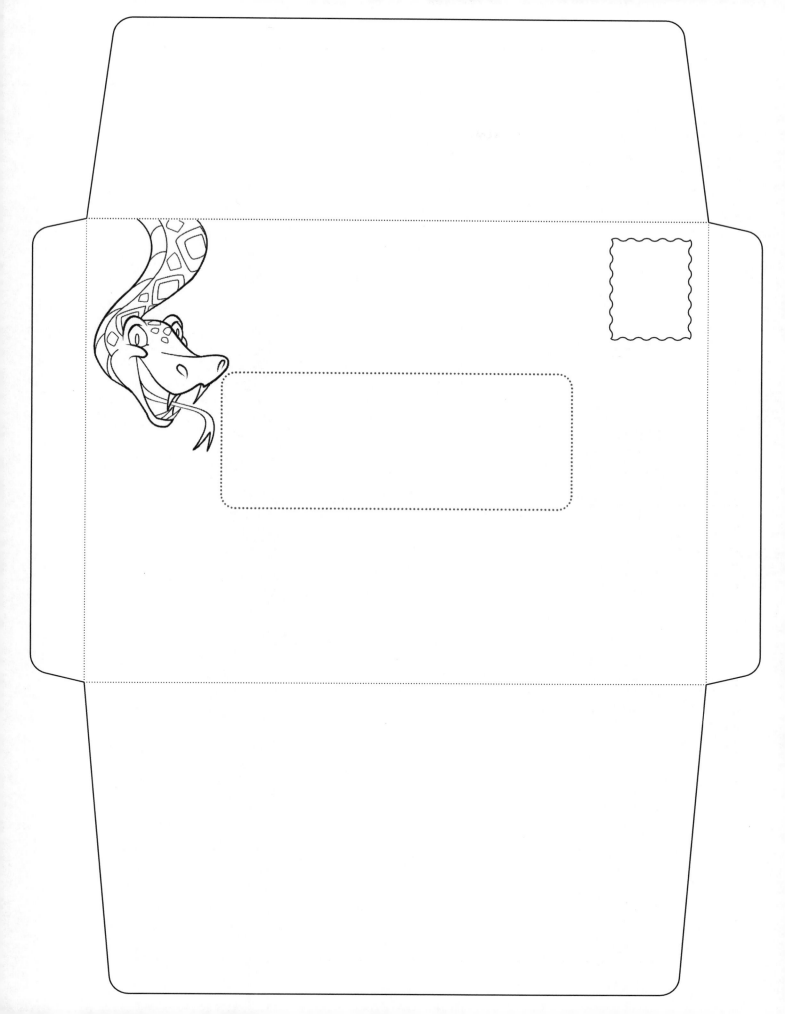

BOTTOM FLAP

THIS CARD COLORED BY

© Top Floor Books

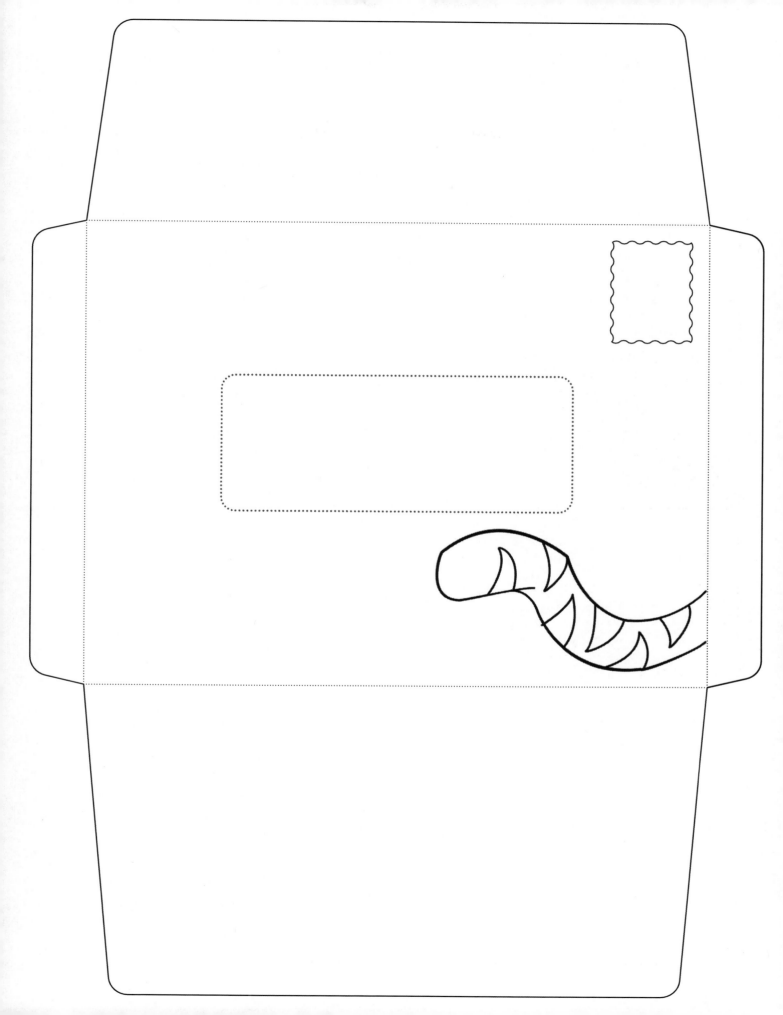

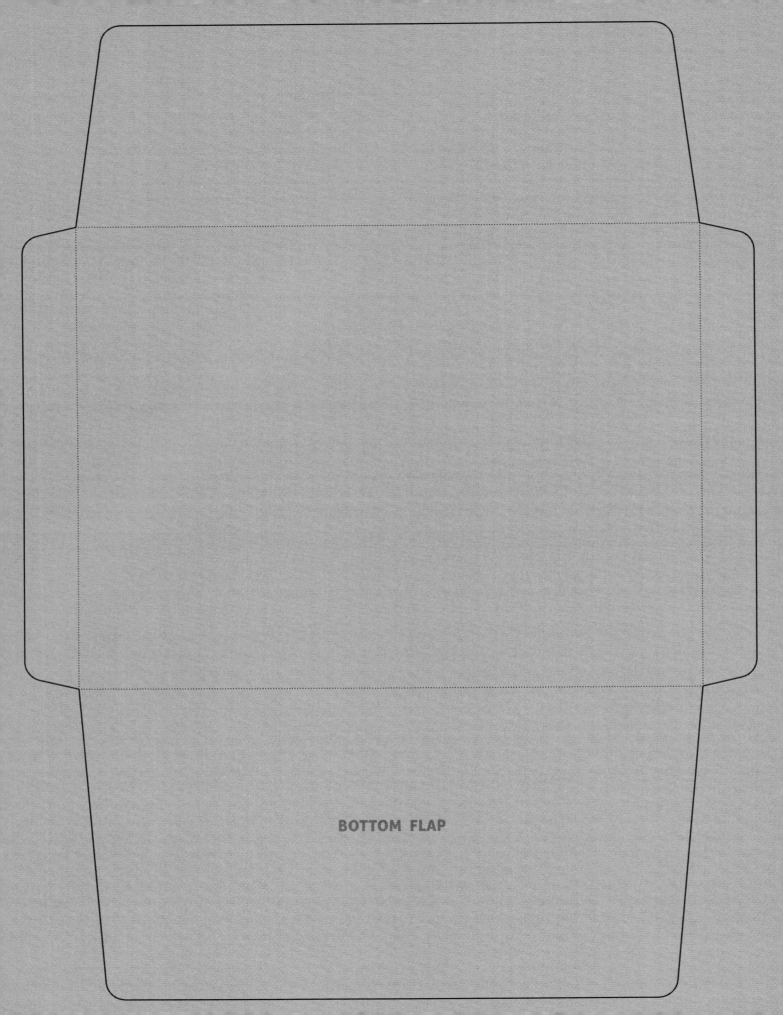

BOTTOM FLAP

THIS CARD COLORED BY

© Top Floor Books

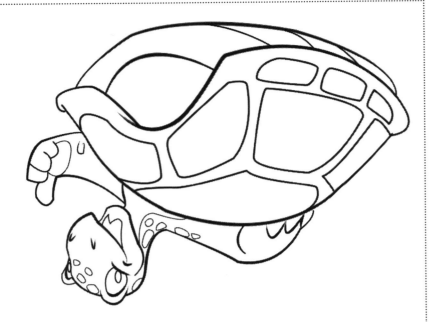

IT'S TIME TO
SHELL-ABRATE!

BOTTOM FLAP

© Top Floor Books

THIS CARD COLORED BY

HANG IN
THERE!

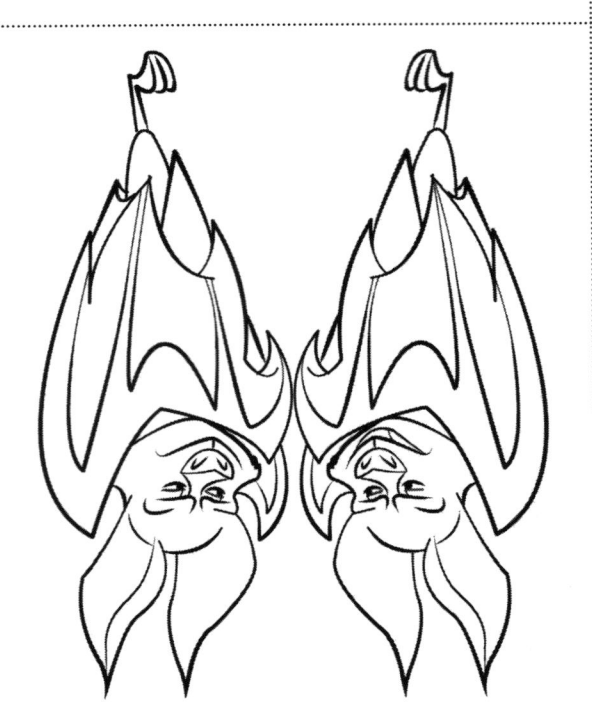

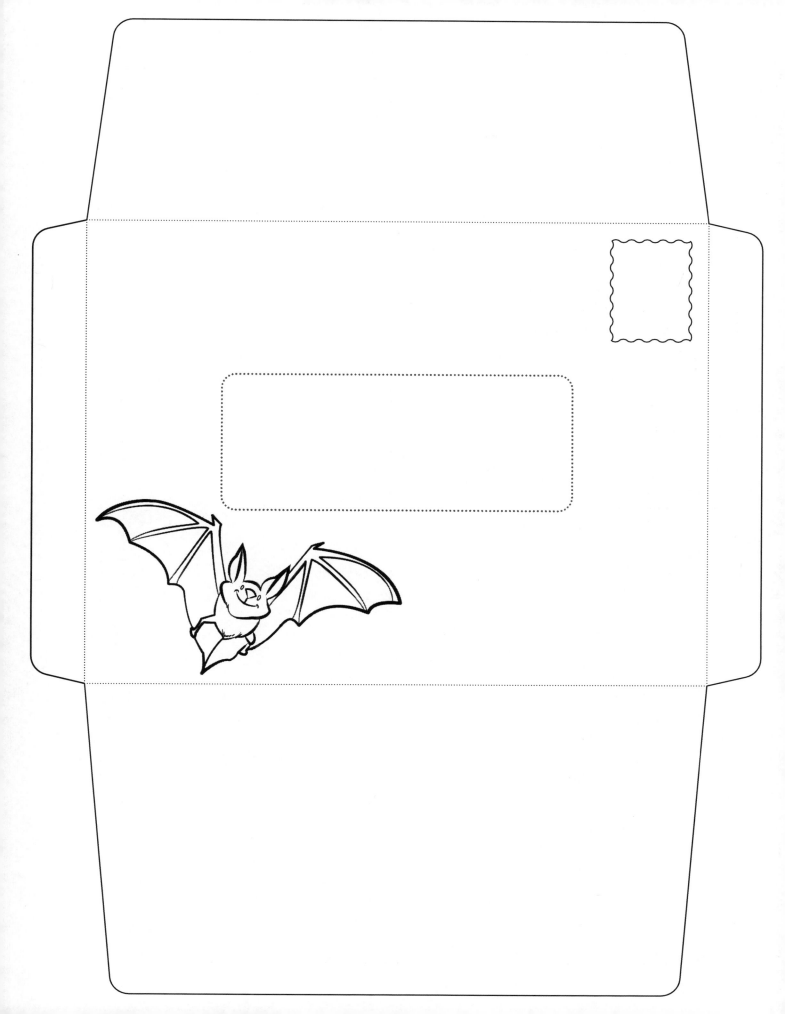

BOTTOM FLAP

THIS CARD COLORED BY

© Top Floor Books

I CAN'T *BEAR* IT WITHOUT YOU

BOTTOM FLAP

© Top Floor Books

THIS CARD COLORED BY

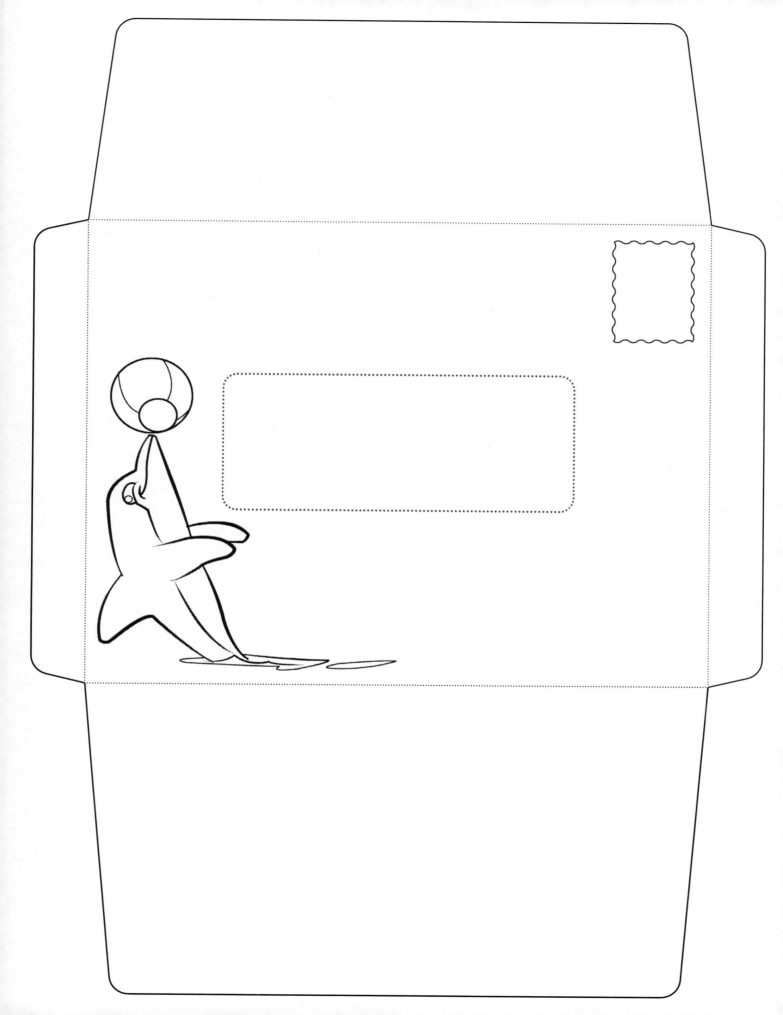

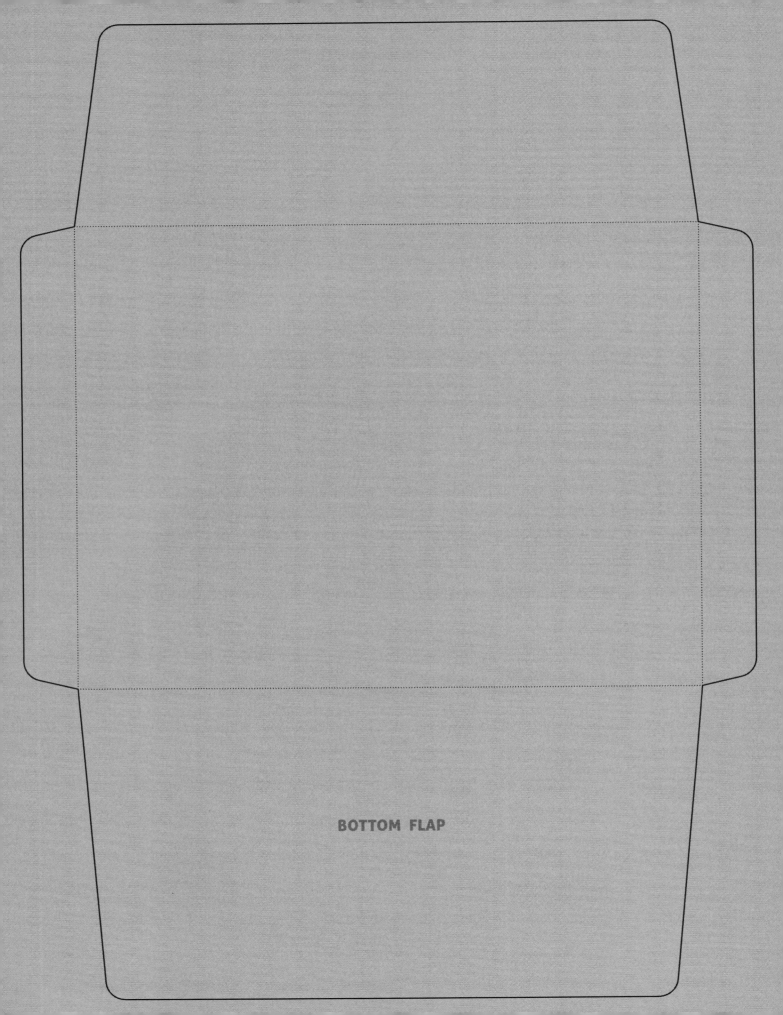

BOTTOM FLAP

THIS CARD COLORED BY

© Top Floor Books

TAKE IT EASY

BOTTOM FLAP

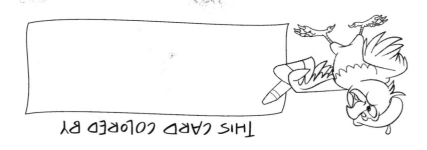

THIS CARD COLORED BY

© Top Floor Books

Time's fun when
you're having flies

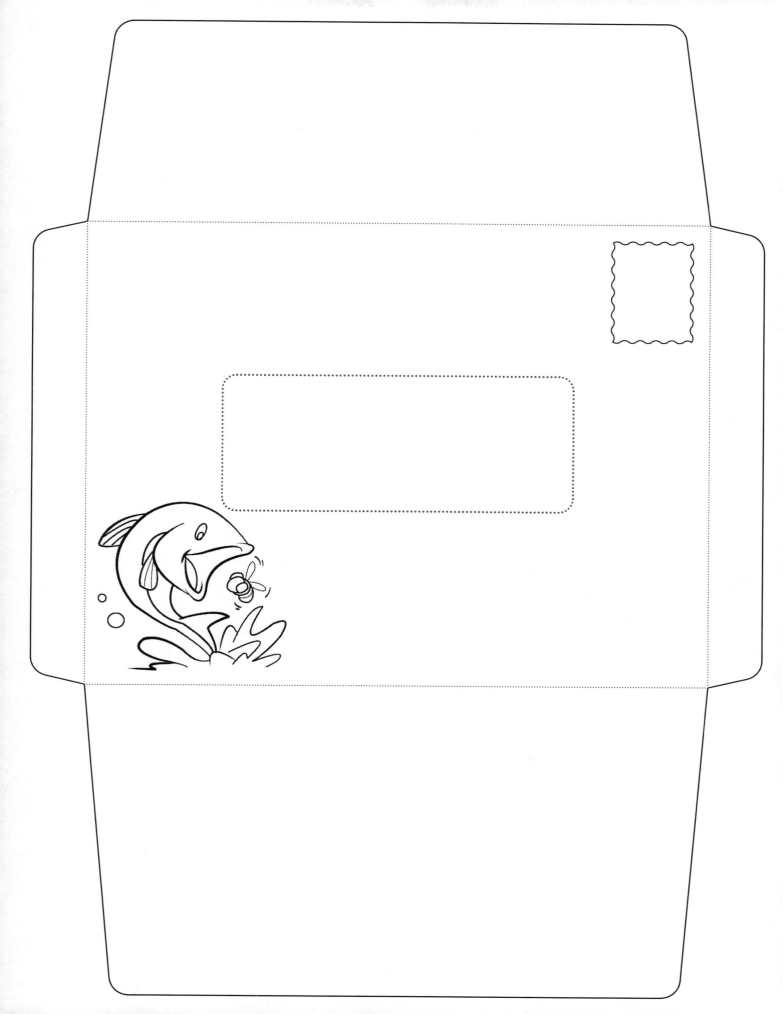

BOTTOM FLAP

© Top Floor Books

THIS CARD COLORED BY

DON'T WORRY
BE HAPPY

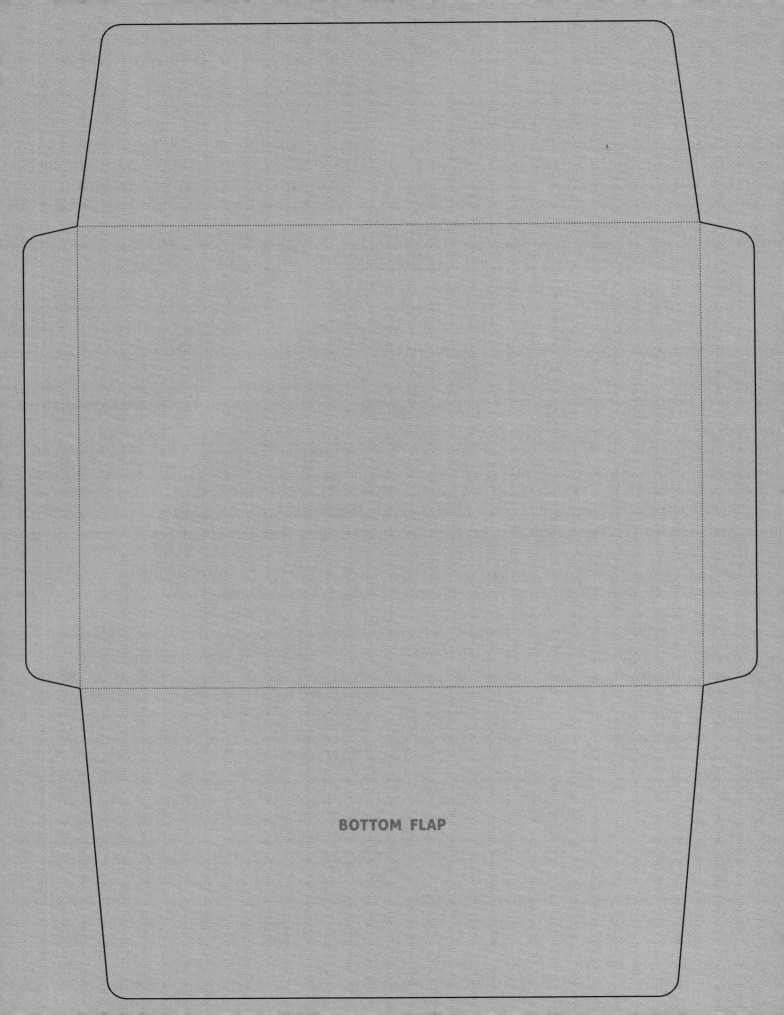

BOTTOM FLAP

SCARLETT McCAW

FLORENTINO GOPEZ (artist)

His career began at age 6, when his cousin discovered him drawing on the ground with barbecue sticks. He wisely switched to pencils and pens, and since then worked all over the world for major animation studios such as Walt Disney and Cartoon Network. He has illustrated children's books and received awards as an animator and illustrator. His guitar and ukulele playing are as funny as his drawing.

M.D. WHALEN (writer)

He was always the kid who sat in the back of the class scribbling stories and cartoons. Later he sat in front of the class scribbling stories, when he should have been teaching! Now he writes full time in the back of his house, and has published many books for children and adults under different names. He always loved coloring as a kid, so he came up with the ideas in this book, and hopes you'll have as much fun coloring it as he will.

Made in the USA
Columbia, SC
09 September 2020

19942804R00070